THE ANGEL OF

Christmas

Roger Blair Johnson

The Angel of Christmas
Copyright © 2022 by Roger Johnson.

Published by: Road Scholar Publishing Group LLC
P.O. Box 25243
Scottsdale, AZ 85255
Reboh@cox.net

Address all inquiries to: reboh@cox.net

Hardcover ISBN: 978-0-9671100-4-2
Paperback ISBN: 978-0-9671100-7-3
ebook ISBN: 978-0-96711005-9

Book Cover & Interior Layout: Fusion Creative Works, fusioncw.com

Every attempt has been made to properly source all quotes.

Printed in the United States of America

First Edition

2 4 6 8 10 12

Dedication

This book is dedicated to Autumn-Paige Alexandria Johnson.

You were a little angel to all who met you and in caring for you during your short time on Earth, I learned the truest definition of what unconditional love feels like. You died far too young, but I know you are having fun flying on the backs of the angels in heaven.

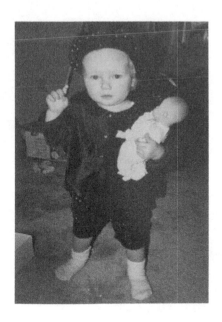

The Angel of Christmas

"Jedi One, climb and maintain flight level three six zero (36,000 feet) and contact Montreal Center on two three four point five, Merry Christmas," said the Bagotville radar controller.

"Two thirty-four point five and back at ya, Merry Christmas," I said.

I was climbing through 10,000 feet as I switched to Montreal Center. I burst through the highest reaches of the clouds just as I switched over to Montreal's frequency. The clouds rapidly descended below me as I ascended into a star-studded sky above at 400 knots airspeed. A very bright, almost blinding, full moon greeted me as I burst into a moonlight that was softly bathing the pillowy looking cloud tops below. Multi-grayish tones of white, black, and every shade in-between defined and painted the cloudscape below, showing the soft undulations of a gently rolling sea of clouds, that stretched from horizon to horizon. It was such a beautiful sight and one that I never tired of being privileged to see.

I had been at Canadian Air Force Base Bagotville for far too long. What was supposed to have been an overnight visit by me to drop off some parts for another F-16 that needed repair, turned into a three-day affair after my Viper developed electrical problems as I was getting ready to leave with the other six Vipers of my squadron. They departed on schedule, but I got stuck for two days while a couple of maintenance guys trouble shot the problem with my aircraft.

Christmas was rapidly approaching and I wanted to get home and be with my wife and young daughter. It was my 17-month-old daughter's first Christmas season where she was realizing there was something "special" about this coming Christmas and I couldn't wait to see the look of surprise on her face as she opened presents, brought to her by Santa Claus. So, I encouraged, bribed, and pleaded with the maintenance guys at Bagotville to do whatever they could to get my jet fixed and get me out of there. Late in the afternoon on Christmas Eve they said the jet was fixed and I could be on my way. I'm sure they were as happy as I was that I was leaving.

As the clouds continued their retreat below and I climbed through 30 thousand feet, the stars, like various sized diamonds laid upon a black felt background, began to show their brilliance. It's funny but every-time I fly at night and gaze upon the brilliance of the Milky Way, I recall the words my agnostic father. When I was kid, he said the only time he felt like there was a higher power was when he looked at the heavens from the cockpit of whatever aircraft he was flying at the time.

As a beautiful touch to the exquisite jewels shinning all around me as I climbed into low earth orbit, the north-ern lights, which were dancing off the right side of the aircraft, were putting on quite a show. Seeing the brightly luminescent curtains of lengthened veils caused me to think I was privy to watching the angels dry their laun-dry in a gentle breeze coming from God's own breath. Curving ever so slightly, or sharply in the magnetic lines of force in the far upper reaches of the atmosphere, the multilayered rows of glowing veils changed their dimensions continuously. While either descending rapidly or retreating back to the stars above, their soft hues changed constantly in luminescence with each undulation of their form and in rhythm to the unheard singing of the angels. The heavenly descending and then ascending veils of luminescent white and pale green waved rhythmically in brilliance. It was always captivating to see the Northern Lights rhythmic display of light and movement. I couldn't help but be mesmerized as I climbed to my cruising altitude this night. I felt I was privy to a world preparing for the birth of His son.

"Montreal, good evening, Jedi One is with you leaving 30 thousand for three six zero."

"Roger Jedi One, maintain three six zero."

"Montreal Jedi One has a request," I added after repeating the initial cruising altitude.

"Jedi One, go ahead with your request," said the controller in a monotone sort of voice.

"So, Montreal, it's Christmas Eve, any chance I could get INS direct to McConnell?" I ask in a very contrite manner.

"Jedi One, fly heading two six zero for now and I'll check on that request"

"Roger," I simply said back.

I reached 36 thousand feet less than ten minutes after takeoff. Once there I engaged the autopilot which held my altitude and my heading. I was flying an early, block fifteen ADF model Viper, and all it had was heading and altitude hold.

"Jedi One, cleared direct McConnell Air Force Base, maintain flight level three six zero and contact Montreal now on two five five point zero. Happy Holidays," said Center, again in a monotone sort of voice.

"Merry Christmas Montreal, two five five point zero" I simply said.

"Montreal, good evening, Jedi One level three six zero, proceeding direct to McConnell."

After being cleared to McConnell and checking in with the new air traffic controller, I put McConnell's latitude and longitude in the INS (Inertial Navigation Computer) and immediately got a course, 250 degrees, and a distance, 1300 nautical miles, to my destination. These numbers (course and distance) were displayed on both the HSI and HUD (Heads Up Display). I consequently put pressure on the side stick controller to turn the aircraft to fly a heading that would track the course in the HUD; once on the appropriate heading, I let the aircraft go back to straight and level, so as to fly the appropriate heading.

"Good evening, Jedi One, maintain three six zero."

Since the model Viper I was flying didn't have the capability to display my exact position on a computer-generated map displayed on either a CRT or flat panel display, I kept track of my position by using a TACAN (**TAC**tical **Air N**avigation). TACANs are UHF transmitters that emit 360 degree "radials", one radial for each degree of the compass rose. These electronic radials enable military aircraft to fly a fairly precise ATC (Air Traffic Control) designated route, Jet route, which are like highways in the sky, and by using multiple TACANs, these routes can extend across North America. Commercial, General Aviation, and Military aircraft fly from a departure airport to a destination using one of thousands of designated Jet Routes. Non-military aircraft use VORs (**V**HF **O**mnidirectional **R**ange which are like TACANs except they use the VHF frequency spectrum) instead of TACANs, but the two types of transmitters are usually co-located and called VORTACs. In addition to emitting electronic radials, TACANs (and VORs) also transmit distance from the station. Thus, having the magnetic position and distance from the TACAN being displayed on the HSI (Horizontal Situation Indicator) in the cockpit, the pilot can maintain a very accurate awareness of his/her position from the selected TACAN station. There are hundreds, if not thousands, of TACANS scattered across North America and it is these TACANS that have allowed military aircraft to fly seamlessly to their destination on electronic highways in the sky over the years.

Nowadays though, GPS (Global Positioning System), INS (Inertial Navigation System), or a combination of both are the primary means in which military aircraft navigate through the skies. Most modern aircraft have both the GPS and INS systems because the GPS refines, more accurately, the position of the aircraft than the INS alone. However, an INS unit is able to allow an aircraft to accurately fly to any point in the world without needing an electronic signal from a ground station or satellite.

A GPS system on the other hand must be able to receive electronic timing signals from multiple satellites in order to give position.

With the above said, whether using GPS, INS or both for navigation, they still use the same Jet routes that were developed using TACANs, but instead of using the TACAN station to navigate on the designated Jet route, they use GPS/INS coordinates which overlay on the TACAN position in order to fly the designated Jet Route. Literally a GPS/INS can fly to any latitude and longitude in the world, unlike a TACAN station which is fixed upon the ground where it was constructed. Finally, since a GPS/INS does not have the "line of sight" limitations inherent in the UHF frequency spectrum, I can use my Viper's INS to navigate to any point in the world without fear of signal loss, the TACAN station malfunctioning, or line of sight issues. That is the reason why I can fly directly from Bagotville to my destination directly and without having to use the TACAN. But the problem is, though I always have distance and course to my destination, it doesn't mean I know exactly where I am at any given moment.

Even though my F-16 does have the aforementioned INS and though very accurate when flying cross country as I was on this flight, I always tuned in various TACAN stations along my route of flight in order to keep me situationally aware of my present position in case there was an emergency and I needed to rapidly find an airport near me upon which to land. Yes, as I said, my INS gave me my position from whatever waypoint I had input into it, like in this case McConnell AFB, but having a digital readout of 1300 nautical miles and a course of say 250 degrees, doesn't help me to know where precisely I am, if I needed to land right away.

As a compliment to the TACAN and INS systems on my aircraft, I also carried paper aeronautical charts with me for my route of flight. Those charts, I carried more than one, had a lot of bits of information on it to include: all the TACANS, VORTACs, or VORs contained with-in the volume of airspace that chart covered; most airports, military and civilian alike; with their runway length and field elevation; jet routes; communication frequencies for various ATC areas; Cities and larger towns; states and their borders; and some geographical markings like larger bodies of water; larger rivers; and mountains.   Plus, a myriad number of other more esoteric bits of information that, to be honest, sometimes I would forget what the notation on the chart means.

The London VORTAC was one such navigational station slightly south of my route of flight and just on the eastern side of Lake Huron (in Canada). I tuned it in so I could follow my progress using both my aircraft's instruments and the chart on my lap. I would usually stuff it on one side of the cockpit or the other when I didn't need to reference it.

"Jedi One, contact Toronto on two five zero point one,"

"Montreal could you give me a Victor frequency? I feel like listening to whatever other airline traffic may be flying this evening."

"Roger Jedi One, contact Toronto on one two eight point six, good night," said Montreal with almost no inflection.

"One two eight point six, thanks, good night and Merry Christmas," I said, with some feeling on the Merry Christmas. No reply back, 'Bah humbug to you!' I thought.

"Toronto, good evening, Jedi One with you at three six zero."

"Roger Jedi One, Good evening, maintain three six zero."

'Rha Jaaa," I replied, so cool was I, I thought.

There was not much airline traffic where I was, or so I perceived from the dearth or radio calls on center's VHF frequency. To verify the lack of aircraft in front of me I used the APX electronic interrogation system on my aircraft to interrogate the mode three spectrum of the transponder band and all I saw were three aircraft within 200 miles of my nose.

As the miles to home clicked by at the rate of eight every minute, I gazed upon the stars of Orion's Belt, the Big Dipper and the steadily decreasing distance to the London VORTAC.

I loved flying the F-16, it was like a magic carpet ride. You sat "above" the aircraft with the canopy sill below you and I always felt like I was riding on top of the aircraft and not in it. On night flights and when flying at high altitude I felt like I was immersed in a sea of stars. The HUD, Heads Up Display, which glowed pale green in front of me gave me most of the information I needed to successfully fly in any kind of weather, I really didn't have to look down into the cockpit too much.

When I did look down upon one of the Viper's instrument panels, which were on my left, right, and in front of me, I was greeted with the soft glow of the aircraft's instrument lighting. On each of the panels were a multitude of knobs, dials, pushbuttons, and flat panel (weapons) displays which controlled all the various systems on the small fighter. In addition, I had a beautiful dimly glowing radar display directly in front of my left knee (in the Viper you recline on a 30-degree angle in the ejection seat, consequently your legs are splayed out in front of you, to the left and right of the forward, lower instrument panel, as if sitting back in a Barcalounger), continuously scanning left and right, searching for aircraft. In contrast to the minus 60-degree temperature of the 600 MPH breeze blowing by my jet at 36,000 feet, the subtle illumination from the cockpit displays surrounding me combined with the stars above and the pleasant temperature of air flowing in from the air conditioning system caused me to experience an emotional warmth that no mere earthbound mortal can understand.

On each flight in the F-16 I became addicted to my body's continual and natural production of opiates, endorphins, due to the very essence of the environment in which I operated. What I am going to say next may sound odd to someone with a much less tumultuous past than myself, but I always felt an overwhelming peace come upon me every time I flew due to my addiction.

As the miles ticked by, I was stargazing at the Milky Way that was directly above. At 36,000 feet I felt like I was in orbit and that brought the stars seemingly closer, brighter, and more detailed than on the ground. As I said earlier, my father said every time he flew at high altitude and stared upon the stars, it was the only time when he believed in a 'Divine Power.' Whose God the Divine Power was; Jewish, Muslim; Christian, or ancient Greek I'll never know since he always felt uncomfortable when talking about religion. However, since my dad never exhibited any behavior remotely associated to the Christian faith while not flying, I think his idea of Divine had more to do with how he felt about the actual view than in any deity that may have created it.

Regardless of my father's lack of religious belief, every time I flew and looked at Orion's Belt it reminded me of evenings spent in the backyard with the old man, listening to his adventures of flying DC-6s, DC-4s, DC-3s, or C-46s, and then as a follow-on to those older aircraft his stories of operating the B-727 or CV-880 around this world of ours. So many stories! He usually told me his aviation tales outside our house, under the stars and while on our patio while he drank himself drunk. He'd always look up and point to the Orion cluster and then, as soon as he pointed to the "belt" he would look at the Big Dipper. From the Big Dipper he would look at the lip of the ladle and then follow an imaginary line to the North Star. In his many tall tales he would proclaim how he used the North Star to help him cross the Atlantic.

How truthful he was, about him using the North Star to navigate, I'm not sure, because many times he made mentioned of using a powerful NDB (Non-Directional Beacon) on the southern tip of Greenland to guide him to Europe. But, no matter how he actually navigated across the oceans, whether by using the stars, NDBs, or the skills of the navigator who was part of the crew, I don't care. What is more personally important to me is that he instilled in me the sub-conscience act to always locate, if I could, the North Star when I flew.

While you may, "Euuuu and Ahhhh," and say, "Wow your father was so cool he must have been a great dad," hold your horses on that hyperbole of assumption.

In the aviation realm, when he began to teach me to fly when I was 16, there is no doubt he was an amazing instructor and has no peer. I can say that now since over the years and having had many instructors after him, the test of time has upheld my father's superior ability as a flight instructor; simply put, the man is gifted.

More importantly, at least to me, though is the fact that my father is an outstanding pilot. There is an adage that says those that can't "do", teach. My father, however, could walk the talk he taught, not just talk it. Those are not just my words of praise they are also the accolades from his peers over the years. I was my father's shadow when he was at work and when I flew on his aircraft, in his jump-seat, while he was the Captain, as I matured. So many times, his colleagues would pull me aside and tell me what an exceptionally gifted pilot he was, 'natural' was also another oft used compliment that was dovetailed in conjunction with gifted. You could probably assume, since I was a kid, my father's colleagues were just trying to be nice to me, but, over the years, particularly after I began to fly in the civilian and then military realms of aviation, I saw for myself the gift of wings God bestowed upon the man. No matter what the aircraft, he flew it as if his whole body was integrated with it. His natural ability never ceased to amaze me.

But, on the flip side, after my father left the airport boundary he morphed back into a mere mortal. Many of my après training flight debriefs with him were accomplished in a strip joint near the airport with the likes of Upside Down Norma, Tiffany, or Bambi dancing on the stage above us, teasing a hormonal sixteen year old boy with their mostly bare curves.

My father thought it was great and he invited the ladies down to us after they danced so I could see, smell, and touch certain areas of those well-built beauties. Since Upside Down Norma had the first breast implants I'd ever seen (in person), my father thought it was important that he point out how well Norma's breasts defied the pull of gravity while she danced upside down. We usually left the strip joint with my father drunk and me hoping one day I could have a woman like Bambi.

In the final resolve, my father was a narcissistic alcoholic whose mood swings could take him from heavenly realms to the center of hell. Even though no one believes me, the man is drunk by 9PM, 360 out of the 365 days that define a year.

People are so funny. When they see a picture of me when I was eight years old with my family at the beach... mother, father, and two sisters and we're all smiling they say, "Aww, you guys all look so happy."

Let me tell what you don't see are the tears of the clowns, my sisters and me. In the darkness of our rooms, day or night, and depending upon my father's mood swings, we would hide in our closets crying in fear as our parent's started screaming obscenities at each other. Invariably my mother began throwing dishes at my father and he would respond by throwing punches. The police were almost a weekly occurrence at our house of hell.

There was one memorable night when I was seven when the police never showed but should have. It was the night my father almost killed my mother. I had to stab him in the back with scissors to keep him from killing my mother by strangulation. I was in my closet hiding when I heard and felt the thump of bodies hitting the floor. I ran from my bedroom and saw my mother flat on her back struggling against my father's hands which were tightly clasped around her neck; I will never forget the stark fear in her eyes as she struggled for life. Looking down upon and on top of her was my father with absolute hatred in his eyes. It was not my angelic, aviator father that I saw at that moment, but an evil demon intent on killing. Seeing my mother's plight, I went to the nearby kitchen and grabbed a pair of scissors my mother kept on the counter, sharp scissors. I stabbed my father on the upper right side of his back, going as deep as I could. A rib stopped the point of the scissors from going into his lung. After the stab, my father released his grip and began crying, an overwhelming sobbing cry such I never heard before or since. Evidently the trauma from the stab wound brought him back to his senses.

So there the three of us sat, on the floor, after my first and only attempt at killing my father after his first, and only attempt at physically killing his second wife. I was crying, my father was bleeding and crying, and my mother gasping for air. On that horrible night they vowed they would never fight again, unfortunately that promise lasted all of a week. But I must admit, I am an optimist and always believed that they meant what they said, it took me until I left for the USAF, at 22, when I realized my parents would never change.

Pat Benatar wrote a very apropos song about my life while growing up in my father's house… Hell is For Children. You see, while I was young my father only picked on my mother, but once I entered high school, and for some unknown reason, he began to randomly attack me in the same manner in which he attacked his wife.

There were only two special situations when peace with Ken was assured, drunk or sober, and that was when he was on an airport's boundaries or when he began reminiscing about his aviation past. My father, unlike my mother, had an unquenchable fire of self-loathing burning in his soul, a fire that burned even hotter when fueled by alcohol and which affected every area of his life, except when he flew or told his stories. The evenings when he went into detail and told me of his flying adventures were not only my wonderfully special, quality times with him, but also the times when I felt most safe from his physical or verbal wrath while at home. I must add, that I never, ever saw the man drink alcohol and then go fly. A far as I know, he never flew closer than eight hours after his last drink. When arriving at an airport, whether to fly or visit, I am convinced angels kicked the demons that normally controlled him off his back, and then they, the angels, took over. His persona while at an airport showed not one scintilla of a personality disorder.

Try as I might over the years and after many huge battles on my part with him to get him to stop drinking and recognize his emotional/personality flaws, he never once admitted to doing anything wrong with either his wife or me, and never apologized for some of his extreme behavior. The day I left his house and went into the military, after college, is the most liberating feeling I've ever had in my life.

But, tonight, despite all the negativity with which I grew up, and in honor of ancient aviators, my father included, who flew low and slow while they blazed new air-routes across this world of ours, I do the same as my father and locate the very same stars by which they navigated. I located Orion's Belt, the Big Dipper and then star stepped my way to the North Star. And, just as it should be it is on the right side of my jet, maybe three o'clock position. Isn't it funny the little things we do and think about while occupying our time between the more important tasks in our daily lives.

A call from Toronto Center with the necessity to switch to another frequency, brought me out of my deep introspective thoughts.

I took a quick break from daydreaming (night dreaming?) to check on my groundspeed and fuel in order to make sure I would have enough "gas" to get home without having to land short and refuel. I was heading into a wind that was supposed to reach a maximum of 125 knots and come from my two o'clock position. While not a showstopper in reaching my destination without a fuel stop, if the wind came more on my nose or got much stronger, I'd be looking at my fuel figures with much more scrutiny. As it was, I estimated I'd arrive at McConnell with between four and five thousand pounds of fuel, more than enough.

In actuality fuel really shouldn't be an issue with this flight. I was equipped with three external fuel tanks, 13,000 lbs of fuel in total when combined with what my jet carried internally. That amount equated to roughly four hours flying time, more than enough for my return flight.

After getting squared away on my navigation and fuel burn issues, I checked on my progress across Canada. The London VORTAC was close, which meant that I was almost out of Canada and that much closer to home.

I am so excited at the prospect of spending Christmas Eve with my daughter and reading her stories by the Christmas tree while eating my wife's wonderfully calorie laden, holiday butter cookies.

Just before coasting out of Canada, I asked Toronto Center if they could give me the present weather and forecast for my destination. Normally I would call a Flight Service Station or a military base's weather shop to do that and not bother ATC, but since the controllers were not very busy, I didn't feel it would be too much of an imposition.

The controller came back relatively quickly with McConnell's forecast of clear skies, but cold conditions and indeed the latest weather observation supported that forecast. However, I've had some pretty bad experiences in the past when a USAF weather specialist had forecast great weather at my destination, only for me to discover upon reaching that destination it was being clobbered by thunderstorms or socked in with low ceilings and fog. When you're leading a four ship of fighters to a destination that you think is going to have good weather, you tend to arrive with the minimum of fuel. Having crap weather when you arrive with low fuel tends to age you very quickly since getting all the aircraft into that base, or diverting, creates a hellish kind of stress that must be experienced to understand. I had my fair share of surprises in my relatively early days of fighter flying, so experience now begets wisdom and I now tend to check my destination's weather with more regularity than I used to.

I resumed my introspective thoughts after getting the weather report, which remained the same as when I left Bagotville. As soon as ATC gave me the weather, I saw a shooting star pass brilliantly overhead and break into smaller and smaller pieces as the Earth's atmosphere quickly devoured it. Seeing the death of the meteor caused me to think of the birth of my daughter and how she arrived like a shooting star upon my world. I never knew I could love a human as much as I love her and I can't wait to see the smile on her face as I come through the door. She has recently begun to say 'HIIIEEEEEE', when I came home from work then lifts up her arms wanting a hug and ride on daddy's shoulders.

I'd been a reluctant father, hell, for that matter I was a somewhat reluctant husband. I met Lisa, my wife, in a Hooters on a Friday night when I was out with the boys while I was going through USAF Fighter Lead in Training. She was a senior in college and working as a server to help pay for college. She said Hooters was the best place to earn big tips in the relatively small, mid-American college town, being drop dead beautiful didn't hurt either. I fell immediately in lust with her, like every straight man did when they saw her. She said Hooters wasn't her dream job, just a means to an end since she was getting a degree in psychology with the intention of eventually becoming a psychologist. I told her I was willing to be a volunteer for her psychotherapy thesis because I was pretty screwed up. Whereupon she added that from her observations most fighter pilots were pretty screwed up...we had a good laugh over that. I was instantly smitten with her from that night on.

We had such a hot and heavy dating life it caused both of our heads to spin and with-in four months of having our first date and right after she graduated from college and before I went away to F-4 Flight training, we eloped. I just couldn't bear the thought of leaving such a beautiful woman in the rearview mirror with all the other fighter pilots who would come after me.

I truly think Lisa was the far more mature one of the two of us since she never looked back after we got married, but, a year after we said "I do", I began to feel we had married too young. I had such a nagging in my heart that I had never sown those wild oats I'd been told about by the dancers at the strip joint. No doubt Lisa's looks and body had me hooked on the first date, reminding me of my sweet sixteen crush on Bambi, the dancer from my strip club days with my father. But, once married and ensconced in the suburbs, life got stale, at least for me.

And of course, once settled into my first active-duty fighter assignment, with the prospect of not moving for a few years, there was the inevitable question from Lisa, 'Are we going to have kids?'

"Ugh."

After her question I dropped a bombshell on her and said that I didn't want them (kids), though that contradicted to what I said to her while we dated when our nude bodies were comingled in passionate embraces. I totally admit during our hot and heavy dating days, when we made both tender and raunchy love in just about every place we could get away with and as much as we could, I spoke careless whispers, never realizing she would believe words uttered from a man intoxicated on both hormones and alcohol. She never pushed or nagged about wanting children after I told her I didn't want any. No, she was silent and dignified in her screams and prayers to a God I could not relate to nor wanted to. Lisa lived her Christian faith with dedication and love since she never treated me with distain, emotional distancing, or bitterness in spite of what I promised before we married. Before we had our daughter though, she did have a child…me.

I wasn't the greatest husband in the early years of our marriage acting grossly immature and childish as hell, and even as I fly this flight, I'm still not much better. Every Friday night at the Officer's Club I act like a child with Prince's song, 1999, my theme song and getting crazy with the boys my usual routine, and that's just at my home base's Officer's Club.

When I go TDY (military trips) I get even more nuts; carousing, pulling pranks on my squadron mates, bar hopping, flirting with women. There is a fire in my soul, an emotional burning that only flying fighters seems to tame, not people, or alcohol, or things. In fact, drinking only fuels the burning desire for something other than my wife, not quenches it. Maybe, while flying the F-16, do I get relief from my emotional storms because I am totally alone and closer to the heavens? It is always while flying do I feel closer to a God that I secretly and desperately want to wholeheartedly embrace, like my wife, but upon landing, the darker side of me takes over and manipulates me like a marionette. I'll never understand why Lisa hasn't left me, never. I'm a supreme ass at times, and though I do apologize, unlike my father with his wife, it's ground hog day, week after week, month after month. Just how long Lisa will tolerate my behavior, I don't know.

My wife is the golden child. Her faith unshakable and her strength of character beyond reproach; quite honest-ly what she sees in me I'll never understand. She had a rough upbringing, due to living with an alcoholic mother who neglected her and a father who left when she was 10, never to return to see her or her siblings again. Lisa was the oldest of three and consequently her mother put the burden on her to mostly raise and care for her younger brother and sister. Being relieved of the burden of having to constantly care for her children, her mother would frequently go out with other men, either for the night or the weekend, leaving a child in charge of two other children.

The hell my wife endured while growing up I can't image and the responsibility she bore while caring for her younger brother and sister caused her to mature beyond her years as she grew into a woman. It was in those grueling years with her abusive and neglectful mother where Lisa turned to reading the Bible on her own, and in fact purchased a study Bible to help her understand what she couldn't when she read the Bible. She had no religious guidance from anyone while in her grade school years, but at the urging a close friend in high school she began attending church with her and their family and in that church a pastor preached about a God who deeply loved her. It was a love she had so desperately craved while growing, and a love of which she showered in spades upon her siblings, trying to make up for what her mother and non-existent father never gave.

My mother, like Lisa's, was no saint either. She was a young flight attendant when she met my married father who was the captain on her first trip after being released to fly the line without supervision. My father fell madly in love with her from their first meeting and with-in a year he was divorced from his first wife and married to my mother, who was now pregnant. I was the third of three children she never wanted. Her idea of the perfect life, pre-marriage, was to fly around the world as a flight attendant and see the sights. My father's vastly different idea was for her to be a stay-at-home wife and mother. My father kind of won the war on the battle of the life-styles, but his dominance over my mother was fret with an extreme amount of personal in-fighting and violence between the captain and the flight attendant. After I was born, five years after they married, my mother asked her older sister if she and her husband wanted to adopt my two sisters and me. My father was not privy to that request. My Aunt and Uncle declined. My mother, like my father, was a narcissist at least this diagnosis (my father's too) coming from a shrink who met both of my parent's when Lisa and I did a brief stint of unsuccessful marriage counseling a couple of years ago.

As an aside, when the psychologist began a deep dive into my childhood, I walked out; there are some memories from my youth that I felt should never be brought to light with anyone and I wasn't about to get into some touchy, feely Dr Phil conversation with a man I barely knew about them. Fighter pilots don't do feelings I believed.

My mother abruptly told me over morning coffee one day, when I was 24, if she could have aborted all of her kids she would have. She said she never wanted them and had multiple affairs on my father to prove her distain for having a marriage in which kids were a part. Many times, she left us for another man while we were at school and while my father was on a trip. My oldest sister then had to take over and care for us until my father returned. Invariably, my mother, would return home when her money ran out, or the man she left my father for dumped her. I asked my father, once I got in the Air Force and didn't have to deal with seeing my mother, why he kept taking her back and he said because he loved her. I'll never understand that kind of love. My mother and I were mutually happy when I left home once I entered the USAF. She hated having kids around and I hated being around her.

Unlike Lisa, neither one of my parents were religious. Oddly though, when I was seven years old and a short time after I stabbed my father, my mother taught me the Lord's prayer. I was seven… what parent arbitrarily does that? I'd never seen her go to church and she's teaching me the Lord's Prayer? My mother spoke softly, next to me, for a few months after she began to kneel with me while we prayed the prayer every night just before I went to bed. I think it's about the only time I got true quality time with her in my life. To this day I subconsciously say the Lord's Prayer when I go to bed, more out of habit than any belief in a higher power. And too, like Lisa, who said while young, on occasion she watched pastors on TV preach, I too watched those same pastors. The only other religious exposure I had in my early years, before meeting Lisa, were the occasional pastor I'd see on late night TV. The reason I didn't change the channel when I saw them preaching on the TV that night was usually due to the fact that I was licking my wounds from a verbal, physical, or both, beatdown from my father that night. There were some very dark days in my high school years when I desperately wanted my life to end. Without question some of those TV preachers gave me a modicum of hope as I listened to their words. Unfortunately, I just couldn't bring myself to believe that God was actually loving, I pictured Him more like my father.

It wasn't until the birth of my daughter, when I saw her "pop out", alien style, from her mother's lower belly due to an emergency C section when I truly fell in love with another human. Anastasia was so innocent and incapable of living without her mother's care and protection. It was at that moment when I knew I had to shed the things of my youth and grow up. God's will for my change, and my wife's secret prayers were answered when I saw my child liberated from the comfort, yet distress, of her mother's womb. However, it has been a very, very slow change on my part.

The decision for me to give in to my wife's desire to have a child came about after we reunited after being separated for six months. Those aforementioned fires and wild oats caused me to leave home with a mission to extinguish the fires and eat my fill of oats. Instead, the oats I ate only added more fuel the internal fires I wanted to snuff out, thusly making my life even more of a living hell, except when I flew; always strapping into the F-16 gave me a welcomed peace. No matter how complicated the mission, how difficult the flight, I feel a supreme calm when strapped into the jet's seat. It is my "church," my alone time with God, even when I fly with one or more wingman. It is the only time I allow God open access to my thoughts and prayers in the sense that is when I "talk" to Him.

After being apart for six months and then reuniting, I felt I needed to give Lisa something she always desired but which she never nagged me about; a child. I almost felt like it was her reward for putting up with my crap. I'll never forget the day she found out she was pregnant, she glowed as brightly as I imagined an angel does.

As my wing tanks fed out and my aircraft lightened up, I requested flight level four zero zero (40,000 feet). Toronto Center immediately cleared me to climb and maintain flight level four zero zero. I was flying at Mach point 87, 87 percent the speed of sound. If I had just the centerline tank, or was clean, no fuel tanks, I'd be flying a Mach point nine or slightly faster, but with the big wing tanks hanging out in the breeze it was more fuel efficient to fly a bit slower, giving me a little more fuel when I arrived at my destination.

The sea of clouds below, which covered every visible square inch of the Earth around me, still remained as I rapidly approached Lake Huron, and the London VORTAC. With the approach of the United States, the northern lights were retreating as I continued southwest with the VORTAC passing slightly to my left, unseen, and far below.

Since I was heading in the opposite direction of the Earth's rotation the moon and Orion's Belt remained relatively fixed in the night sky, almost as if I had painted them on a black ceiling in my house. The moon's soft, yet overwhelming glow was welcomed as it allowed me a view of the planet few people ever get to see. The vast sea of clouds passing below me never wavered in visual texture and uniformity, at least not since I had departed Bagotville. How far down the clouds descended I did not know, nor even cared, since I knew my destination was going to be free of them when I arrived.

As I approached the US/Canadian border Toronto Center switched me over to Minneapolis Center.

"Minneapolis, Merry Christmas, Jedi One with you at four zero zero."

"Jedi One, Merry Christmas, kinda' late to be flying isn't it? Shouldn't you be home?"

"Yeah, well that's where I'm headed now. Shouldn't you be home too?" I countered.

"Well, in about four hours I will be," responded the controller in an upbeat inflection.

It was nice to be in US airspace again. It meant I was making progress in getting home. The winds at my cruising level were howling along at the forecast 125 knots and from the forecast direction. They slowed my ground speed about seventy-five knots. Since I had a true airspeed of about 530 knots, the winds brought my groundspeed back to 455 knots.

I was with the first Minneapolis controller only a short time when he instructed the following: "Jedi One, contact Minneapolis on one thirty-five point four five, happy holidays!"

I had to wait for a couple of aircraft that were talking on the next frequency before I could check-in with Center. Just as there was a pause in the aircraft talking on Center's frequency, and as soon as I keyed the microphone to check-in with my altitude, my aircraft suddenly went dark.

"Christ, what the hell happened?"

I immediately released the microphone switch and looked to see if my engine was running, thinking it had failed and with it the main engine generator. Nope, it was running. That was a relief but, losing the main generator was a big deal, particularly at night with clouds all around. I knew the EPU, Emergency Power Unit, which ran on either hydrazine or bleed air from the engine would give me limited electrical power to get me somewhere, but that question was where is that "SOMEWHERE?"

The EPU was supposed to start automatically after a main generator failure, but I didn't get a run light from it, nor did I see an indication on the tele light panel and the limited number of electrical busses it powers to confirm that it was running. Without referring to the emergency checklist I immediately toggled the switch that was supposed to start the EPU if it didn't automatically come online.

No such luck. Crap.

OK, my plan B was to immediately reset the main generator, which I did.

Sha zamm!!, The generator immediately came online and jump illuminated all the cockpit lights, revived the VHF radio, navigation equipment, and other instruments and displays.

"Whew, I dodged a bullet there I thought. Thank you God for that."

Then I smelled smoke. Then bam!!…lights out again.

"Crap, crap, crap…you've gotta' be shitting me. Please God, not on Christmas Eve," I prayed. I hacked the timer on my cockpit clock. I knew I had a maximum, or so the manual says, of 30 minutes on main battery power.

I thought about resetting the main generator again, but the smell of smoke alluded to a serious electrical issue that could only get worse, in my estimation, if I kept forcing the main generator online. It was intuitively obvious the aircraft's protective circuits were trying to do just that, protect the aircraft, but in protecting the aircraft, it may have screwed itself if I can't find a place to land quickly enough. The loss of my aircraft was now a very real possibility, one in which I prayed would not happen.

I wouldn't have missed the loss of the main generator as much if only the EPU came online, but, it didn't and that's what truly concerned me. The main battery didn't power any navigation equipment and I only had about 30 minutes of juice in it before it would die. I needed to get on the ground ASAP, but lord, where was I and how low did the clouds go before I could break out and see the ground, let alone find an airfield?

I switched back to using the UHF, since the VHF radio doesn't work on battery power, and tuned in 243.0, the UHF aviation emergency frequency. I then began transmitting, "Mayday, mayday, mayday!!" to anyone that might be listening.

Because I was so high, the moon so bright, and the air so clear I had no trouble rapidly descending to the clouds far below while easily maintaining situational awareness of my attitude. The engine was working fine and on battery power the RPM and FTIT, Fan Turbine Inlet Temperature, gauges were operative but the leading-edge flaps were now inoperative due to the emergency so I had to limit my angle of attack to 12 degrees maximum. Unfortunately, my AOA indicator was also inoperative and I was fairly heavy with fuel so I limited my minimum flight speed to 210 knots until I dropped the landing gear and I did not intend to pull many Gs while maneuvering. In fact, I descended at a much higher speed since the clock was ticking with regards to how much time I had on the battery before it failed.

In desperation while in my descent to a lower altitude I cycled the main generator a couple more times, but to no avail, it would not come online, nor could I get the EPU to operate.

I had to keep the UHF radio calls to a minimum, since each time I talked I used that much more battery power than while listening. Minneapolis Center responded to my initial mayday and asked what the problem was. I told them I had an electrical emergency and needed to land with-in thirty minutes, otherwise I was going to have to eject. It was in their response when I felt a sense of hope replaced by dread.

"Jedi One, our primary surveillance radar (skin paint) is inoperative due to maintenance in progress. We only have secondary surveillance ability at this time. Our last transponder fix showed you just east of Alpena, over Lake Huron and heading south, southwest towards Grand Rapids. The weather everywhere, from Michigan, Ohio, Indiana, Illinois, Pennsylvania and Eastern Wisconsin is under a winter storm warning. State your intentions?"

Wow. What a question, "State Your Intentions?" What a loaded question. Well, for one, landing immediately comes to mind, but I wasn't going to be smartass. What could I do? Yes, I had an ejection seat and without question I was going to use it, if it came to that, but that was my last resort. I was going to exhaust every available option, of which, admittedly, there weren't many before I resorted to jumping out of the aircraft.

"Minneapolis, is there a fighter unit on alert that you could launch in order to come find me and lead me back to a base?" I asked with sincerity, knowing though if a fighter could find me, the odds are by the time it did find me and lead me to a suitable landing field, my battery would have died well before reaching that field.

"Jedi One, Roger. We can see if the F-16s that are on alert in Madison will launch and try to find you. Stand by."

That was probably the longest "stand-by" of my life with regards to waiting for ATC to get back to me.

"Minneapolis, could you give me the local altimeter setting for Alpena and the weather?" I asked while waiting for their response to my request for a fighter to find me and bring me safely down

"Alpena is two nine eight zero, the wind is from the east at ten knots. The present weather is indefinite ceiling, one mile in heavy snow, temperature minus three, dewpoint minus four (Celsius). We're talking to Toronto to see if they have a skin paint on you. They have a radar near London, Ontario. We'll let you know."

"Thanks Minneapolis. I'm in a descent to check the tops of the clouds. I'm going to try and penetrate them and see if I can break out below. I have maybe 30 minutes before my battery fails. If I can't land by then, I'll have to eject,"

I said with resignation, feeling almost hopeless after hearing the weather in Alpena.

As I was talking to the controller, I steepened my descent to see how low the undercast went. Michigan is not a mountainous state that I know of, and the east side is particularly flat I thought. I hoped. I prayed. With the power at idle I descended rapidly and while doing so I dialed the altimeter setting of 2980 into the altimeter.

I decided to perform a spiraling descent as I went lower. I flew with less bank, as I headed west by southwest and then steepened my bank as I went through a southerly through northwesterly heading. I did this hoping I would arrive over the landmass of lower Michigan when, or if I had to eject. However, I was afraid if I flew too long to the west I'd wind up over Lake Michigan, on the west side of the lower half of Michigan, so there was a bit of trepidation with what I was doing. I estimated my position as almost halfway down the lower half of Michigan and I gave thought to just heading south as fast as I could and hopefully finding a hole to descend through and then finding an airport south of the state of Michigan.

"Jedi One, Minneapolis Center."

"Go ahead Minneapolis"

"Madison is launching two F-16s that were on alert. They are also launching a tanker from Rickenbacker in support due to the poor weather. The Command post in Madison requests that you orbit your present position. We told them that we estimate your present position as 100 nautical miles northeast of Grand Rapids.

"Roger Minneapolis, I am in a spiraling descent to check the tops of the clouds. I do concur with your estimate, however let the Vipers know I am headed down to below 10 thousand feet. Please have them come up on two forty three zero when they get close."

"Will do Jedi One, they are just taking off now. We'll vector them to where we think you are and will switch them to your frequency when they get closer. Hang in there Jedi, Christmas is the time for miracles"

"Roger Minneapolis, I'm hanging in there," I said flatly.

But, inside I didn't believe I deserved a miracle. God's grace was only reserved for those like my wife, the "good people," who truly believed, not heathens like me. I was anything but deserving of grace from a God I barely knew, or even wanted to know. In the past I didn't want God telling me how to live my life.

As the end of my life rapidly approached, I realized that my nights carousing with the boys in the Officer's Club, or when on trips, meant very little compared to the time I spent -and so little time it was- with my daughter and amazingly beautiful and loving wife.

It's truly remarkable how, when faced with death, you realize how some of the things you've done in your life that seemed important at the time really don't matter and that other things, like the time you didn't spend with loved ones, shines brightly in your soul as a reminder of what you missed. I was overcome with dread as I descended, that I would never see my wife and daughter again and seized with a horrible pain that my fate was relegated to the whims of torturing demons-I deserved as much I thought.

I reached the cloud tops in a couple of minutes. if I wanted to descend into the weather, it necessitated that I have an operative attitude indicator so I knew which end was up in the clouds. However, another problem presented itself. My Viper's main attitude indicator failed when I lost the main generator and the standby attitude indicator, generally called the peanut gauge, had only nine minutes of internal battery power, although it too was powered by the battery bus. So, I really wasn't sure how much time I had before it failed, 9 minutes or 30? Whatever it was I wasn't going to press the time limits on it, so I decided to use ten minutes as it's longevity. Evidently General Dynamics never thought you'd have a total power failure for more than nine minutes.

The cloud tops were at 7,000 feet. I had maybe 8 minutes of standby attitude power left, so I drew a deep breath, pushed the power up and accelerated to 400 knots and then began a descent into the unknown. I began the descent into a layer of clouds that shown whitish grey while above them, but became oppressively black once enmeshed in their turbidity, since the moonlight couldn't penetrate where I was going and I had no exterior lights to illuminate the area around me. I had to stay fast because I didn't have any wing anti-ice capability so I figured going fast would keep ice from accreting to the wings. The engine anti- ice, due to the electrical loss, automatically turned on. I used the standby attitude indicator to help me keep my attitude bearing as I descended. I set the throttle to mid-range in order to maintain airspeed and while leaving the throttle set, I took my left hand off of it and used a small flashlight in my left hand to help me see what few, still operating, instruments I had. I had a utility light with a stretchable power cord, and with an attached clip, I used that clip to mount it to the side of the canopy rail and aim it at whatever area of the instrument panel I desired. Before descending into the weather, I aimed the light at the altimeter and used my handheld flashlight to monitor my airspeed, vertical speed and standby attitude indicator. I continued my east to west holding type pattern as I initially descended, rapidly, to 1,500 feet. I knew there weren't any mountains in the area, but I was worried about tall radio towers. In some places of the country those towers reach over 1,000 feet above the ground. I knew Alpena was around 700 feet above sea level. So, with 1,500 feet on the altimeter I figured I was around 800 feet above the ground. In addition to radio towers, I was worried about other aircraft so I called Minneapolis and told them what I was doing and where I thought I might me. They said there were no low flying aircraft showing on their radar in the area I thought I was in. So, hoping I wouldn't hit a tower I went further down, at 100 foot increments. I was now heading west at 500 feet above the ground, I saw no lights, nothing, just a blackness so deep in hue my eyes hurt due to my pupils trying to expand enough to discern some sort of light. Another 100 feet and then another and still nothing. I was now at 1,000 feet MSL, what I judged as 300 feet above the ground and still I had nothing. Every now and then I did see suffused illuminations of lights from down below. Even though I doubted that I could ever get below this weather, the fact that I saw some semblance of humanity gave me hope that if I had to eject, I would see the ground before I landed on it. That was the good news, but the snow was so heavy and the ceiling so low I couldn't get below the clouds in order to have any hope of finding an airport.

After seeing it was hopeless to descend any more, I pulled the nose up and climbed rapidly to get above the clouds before my standby attitude indicator failed, if indeed nine minutes was its lifespan. As I climbed, I still maintained a slow spiral, now with no bias in heading west since I knew I was over land.

It had been 15 minutes since I lost my generator. Once on top of the weather I circled over an indistinct area above the clouds, not knowing where I was or what was below me. I had run out of ideas and resigned my fate to ejecting. Unless those Vipers found me and were able to get me to a viable landing field in the 15 minutes I estimated I had left on my battery, I was headed for a nylon letdown. I needed a miracle. I prayed to God that I wouldn't die in the ejection, well not the ejection itself, but in the landing, because God only knows what I would land in or on. Powerlines, tall antennae, water, there were a myriad number of ways the ground could kill me while descending in a blinding snowstorm.

I told Minneapolis Center I was going to eject in a few minutes and asked if they had word on the Vipers.

Jedi One, we just switched the Vipers to Guard (243.0) and they are going to try and contact you.

"JediOne, this is Hooter Two One, flight of two, how do you read?"

"Hooter this is Jedi, man am I glad to hear you guys! What is your position?"

"Jedi, we're north of Grand Rapids and heading for the controller's last estimate of your position. What is your altitude? By the way, we are talking to Center on Victor, you won't hear us communicating with them. We want this frequency to be clear, just for communication between us, and probably whatever Navy pilots are flying (that was a known joke through the years that Navy pilots would use 243 as a conversation frequency between aircraft. It wasn't completely untrue).

"Roj Hooter, I'm at 7000 feet and orbiting just above the clouds, I have no idea of my exact position, I might be a bit further north than Center thinks. Guys, I have fifteen minutes left, I need a miracle!"

"It's Christmas Jedi, we got a miracle 2000 years ago with the birth of the Son. He's going to give you one tonight, keep the faith brother."

"Hooter, what kind of radar do you guys have?"

"APG 68, why?"

"Just curious. If you're above me your look down range may be reduced in certain aspect angles due to the Viper's radar cross section."

"No sweat Jedi, we're aware. Just keep a tight orbit."

"Ten minutes boys. Head back to base, there is no time to escort me anywhere. Have a Merry Christmas Hooter."

"Hooter Two One, Two Two has a contact, twenty left for 65 miles, angels seven."

"Hooter Two Two, you have the lead on the right"

"Hooter Two Two, lead on right, burner (meaning go afterburner, to increase speed dramatically), now"

"Roj, Two One's left side, 3,000 feet, visual, sorted."

"Hooter Two One, can you tell me my position? Since you guys have radar contact, I figure you must know roughly where I am," I asked.

"Jedi I was just looking at that. You're about 15 miles southwest of Alpena. Did you copy that too Minneapolis?"

"Minneapolis Center copies."

"Minneapolis, could please do me a favor?" I asked, knowing that Hooter was on the same frequency.

"Yes Jedi One, go ahead," said Center.

"Please, tell my wife, I'm sorry I wasn't such a great husband, that I love her more than she'll ever know, and I'm sorry I never really told her that. Tell her thank her for being such a great mother and for having the most beautiful child in the world. I'm sorry I didn't make it home for Christmas. Can you pass that message along please?"

"You bet Jedi One, we'll pass that message along. We'll alert the local authorities in your area. Good luck sir, we're all praying for you down here."

"Thanks, I need it," I said with resignation.

It was now 20 minutes on the timer since I'd lost my main generator. I knew Hooter was trying their best, but even if they joined on me, there was no possible way they could get me to an airfield that had good enough visibility in which to shoot an instrument approach and land. Most big Airliners had zero/zero autoland capability, but not Vipers. I cinched down my straps in preparation for the ejection and now turned and headed south by southwest. Thanks to Hooter Two One's position update at least I had an idea where I was and that I was over land and not Lake Huron, that was a relief.

Before I pulled the ejection handle between my legs, I said a prayer:

"Dear God, I've made so many mistakes as a husband. I didn't deserve my wife or the beautiful child we have. I'm so sorry for being such a screw-up, for my mistakes. I wish I could make up for all the bad things I've done, please forgive me. Lord if I could go back in time and knowing what I know now, I'd change. I promise if you let me live to see my wife and daughter, I swear I'll change my ways. God, it's Christmas, please!!! I need a miracle, don't let me die tonight and don't let my crashing jet hurt anyone!!"

Right after my prayer to a God I tried to believe in but never obeyed, I saw another shooting star appear in front of me and move from left to right. I followed it as it went to the right side of my canopy and as soon as I looked where the shooting star disappeared, I saw an aircraft, not more than 100 feet away. Quite honestly it startled me and I initially banked left. Then rational thought took over, I rolled out, and looked at the aircraft next to me. I was expecting it to be an F-16, in fact it was a F-4. It had its electroluminescent formation lights on and as I looked forward to the cockpit I could see it only had a pilot, no backseater. I always thought they flew Phantoms with a backseater on night-flights, I also knew, since I had flown F-4s you could fly it single seat, but you lost the ability to use the radar and the bombing computers, as well as the INS for navigation other than one preset coordinate.

"Minneapolis and Hooter Two One, you guys are not going to believe this, but a F-4 just joined on me and wants me to follow him. I'm down to ten minutes or less on battery, I'm going to follow this guy, it's my only hope."

"Jedi One, do not acknowledge this. We are 15 miles away, no way to get you anywhere if we joined up. I don't know who that crazy son-of-a-bitch is flying a Phantom in this weather, but I think you got your miracle son. Give us a call on UHF when you land Jedi. Good luck!"

The F-4 rocked its wings, signaling for me to join into close formation, which I did. I tried to communicate with the aircraft on the UHF but never received an answer.

I initially had my doubts about following the Phantom, wondering if this crazy idiot was going to fly me into the ground. I had no other options though. Time was running out. I had at best ten minutes of battery power so I stayed glued to the Phantom's left wing as we descended into the white fury of the severe winter storm. The clouds were very thick as we descended into them, at times they were so thick the entire fuselage of the Phantom would become dim, almost disappearing with only the green electroluminescence of the formation lights being visible. Only the Phantom had such wonderful formation lights and, on this night, with clouds so thick, the formation lights made staying in position relatively easy. There is no doubt that the pilot of this Phantom was smooth in his flying ability which made it easy for me to stay on his/her wing.

I looked many times at the pilot, never was the look returned, whoever was flying always looked straight ahead. The aircraft had a tiger painted on its nose, I saw that before we descended into the clouds. I had so many questions in my head as to where this rogue jet came from since he didn't answer me on the UHF. This whole experience was surreal I thought as we went down, down, down into a dizzying world of swirling snow. I prayed my wings wouldn't ice up before I landed.

Finally, I could feel I was slowing significantly and leveling off slightly. Lord this pilot was smooth in his/her flying ability, and I thank God for that because I was nervous as hell. I knew I had only one chance at this approach before my battery died so I was a little rough in my own flying. While slowing down, as perceived from having to reduce power on my engine, I saw the Phantom's gear drop and I did likewise, for me I had to drop both the main gear handle and then pull the alternate gear extend, due to the electrical problem. I was relieved when I both felt and heard my gear come down and then saw the three green gear down lights illuminate.

I was worried about the speed being too slow on final approach, since I didn't think the Phantom pilot could possibly know that once my gear was down, I needed to maintain a maximum of 12 degrees AOA, which, since my trailing edge flaps came down with the gear, I could now slow below the 210 knots I previously held as a minimum. I don't know how this Phantom pilot knew what approach speed I needed to fly in order to maintain full control of my aircraft, but he did. So, downward we continued, into an opaque blackness brought on by an overabundance of white snowflakes.

Finally at an altitude that I can only judge by the hair on my neck standing up, runway lights, their small white bobs appearing out of a duller whiteness of swirling snow began flashing by underneath the Phantom. Thinking we were going to do a formation landing I looked briefly at the pilot. He was pointing down with his left hand, which I took as meaning he wanted me to land. We were very low. With no time to spare I looked away from the Phantom and looked forward to see the most beautiful sight I've ever seen…a beautifully wide, brightly lit, snow-covered runway in front of me.

I touched down, not too gently since I still had quite a bit of fuel on board, I really wasn't sure of my angle of attack on landing since I had no HUD or AOA indications. I was just thankful to God that I had a runway underneath. Due to the fairly heavy accumulation of snow, I didn't need to use the brakes since the drag of the snow on my landing gear brought my speed down rapidly and the runway was very long. Oddly, the snow accumulation on the runway was a godsend since it helped to slow the aircraft without me having to apply the brakes. Because of the electrical power failure the brakes were only going to operate on accumulator pressure, so the number of braking applications I had was limited.

The sight outside my aircraft as I slowed to taxi speed on the runway had to be seen to be believed. The snow was falling heavily and obscuring the more distant of the airdrome's lights to the point that some of the more distant lights looked like glowing orbs, either white, the runway lights, or blue, the taxiway lights, with the rotating beacon's white, green, white pulses being suffused in the blowing snow and mist.

Once slowed to taxi speed I added power and looked for a taxiway in which to turn off. I could barely see the outline of a large hanger to my right as I saw a taxiway just abeam it and near the runway's end. I used differential braking in order to turn since the nose wheel steering was inoperative.

I had no clue where to taxi and shutdown. After clearing the runway, I made a radio call on the UHF to let Hooter Two One flight know I had landed. Each of the boys, Hooter Two One and Hooter Two Two, were happy for my safe landing and asked where I landed. I said I didn't know yet it was snowing so heavily. I did tell them the

Phantom did not land, which surprised both them and me.

Again, they wished me a Merry Christmas and then Hooter Two One added, oddly, "If you made any promises to God tonight in order to stay alive, make sure you keep them."

In response I asked him if he was an angel. "No, I'm anything but that. I've been where you are. I didn't learn. I lost my wife and kids years ago because I refused to change. Don't let your family get away. God gave you a miracle tonight, you've got a second chance. Don't blow it son."

I was thinking after that communication with Hooter Two One, that tower or ground control would chime in on 243, but they did not.

As I slowly crept towards the large hanger in front of me, I began to discern smaller buildings to the hanger's left side and taxied towards them. Finally, after nearing one of the buildings, now to my right since I was taxing parallel to the row of large and small buildings adjacent to the ramp I was now on, I saw a sign on one of the buildings that said "Welcome to Wurtsmith AFB."

OK, so now I knew where I was, but why weren't there any other aircraft on the ramp? Did they pull all of them into the hanger?

The building with the welcome sign above it had some lights on. I shutdown the engine once in front of it and set the parking brake. As I prepared to raise the canopy, hoping I still had enough battery power to open it, I saw a person coming out from the double doors that led into the facility.

I exited the jet, after shutting off the battery switch in the cockpit and then closed the canopy with the external switch.

The unknown person I saw coming out of the building came up to the aircraft as I was climbing down.

"Wow, so what brings you to this base on such a stormy night?" said the old man who was wearing a ball cap and a heavy black coat with a fur lined collar.

"Well, I lost my main generator about thirty minutes ago. I was enroute to McConnell Air Force Base. I thought I was going to have to eject but some F-4 joined on me above the clouds and led me in here. Do you have F-4s that sit alert here?" I inquired, expecting a 'yes 'answer.

"Sir, this base was closed a year ago. It's in a caretaker status. Every now and then a C-17 will come in and take some cargo out, but for the most part the base is closed for aircraft operations. I guess one day it'll be a civilian airport, but right now it's closed to all aircraft. How the hell did you get in here with this snow?"

"Like I said, an F-4 led me in. I assume he flew an ILS approach in here."

"No, it's impossible, the ILS was decommissioned, it's a VFR only airport."

"Ok sir, help me out, if this airport is closed, why are all the runway and taxiway lights on including the rotating beacon?"

"Son, it's Christmas Eve, I turned on the lights as my way of displaying Christmas lights on the airport, ya know, brighten the place up and bring in some Christmas Spirit. I used to be stationed here for many years as a base oper-ations specialist. I retired a few years ago and was hired as a civilian contractor after I retired. I know this base like the back of my hand."

As the old timer and I talked I pulled my duffle bag with some clothes out of a travel pod that was hung on one of the stations on the wing of my jet. The snow was still falling with a vengeance with occasional gusts of wind swirling the snowflakes into temporary tornados near the side of the operations building. I got some blocks of wood that were on the side of the operations building and chocked the Viper. As I did all this the gentleman stood at the door to the building.

"Wow we are sure getting one heck of a winter storm, beautiful, isn't it?" said the gentleman as he looked at the sky around us. His eyes closing slightly due to the snow falling on his face.

"Well, if I had been sitting on the ground like most people tonight and since it's Christmas Eve, I'd be playing in this with my wife and daughter, and rejoicing. But, given the fact that I thought I was gonna' die about 45 minutes ago, due to this oppressive blanket of white, I guess beauty is in the eye of the beholder. However, now that I am safe and I didn't have to jettison my jet I can truly say that this is the most beautiful snowstorm I've ever been in." I said that as I looked behind me, and paused, just before I walked into the operations building's door.

"Yes, now that I know I will see my wife and daughter again, this is a lovely snow. I always felt that a blanket of snow washed away the sins of the world upon which it fell, ya know?" I said, surprising myself that I said that to a total stranger.

"Yeah son, I know what you mean. I was pretty wild and crazy in my younger man's enlisted years. I had a lot of sins to atone for when I got older. But then again, isn't that the reason for the season, the birth of the Son and His grace being gifted upon us all?" said this wise old man with a smile, as he put his hand on my back as I entered the building ahead of him.

"Yes sir, it is."

After entering the operations area, I used a telephone to call Minneapolis Center to tell them I had landed at Wurstsmith Air Force Base. They were incredulous that I could find it, when I told them a F-4 led me to it, they were even more shocked. They said they had no transponder contact with any aircraft in the area of Wurstsmith when I was declaring an emergency or talking to them, even when I said I had joined up with the Phantom. They were in the process of checking all of the military bases in the region to find out where the Phantom came from. They finally added that Hooter Two One and Two Two made it safely back to Madison and they didn't have to refuel from the tanker. They said they'd call back if they found out anything on the wayward Phantom.

After talking to the Center, I called my base operations command post to let them know what happened. The Sergeant on duty was greatly relieved that I had landed. I told her, briefly, what happened and how a F-4 led me in here, but to be honest, I don't think she could comprehend what I told her about how I made it into Wurtsmith. Hell, I was struggling, now that the adrenalin was wearing off, as to how I got in here

"Jedi, you should probably call your wife now, we called her and told her you had an emergency and were trying to land somewhere up north, but we had very little information to go on when we talked to her and I think she's pretty upset."

"Yeah, I'm sure she is. I'll call her now. Cheryl, have a Merry Christmas," I said, adding a personal touch to my conversation with the sergeant, since I knew her quite well from my years at McConnell.

"You too Jedi, we're all glad you're safe. The phone's been ringing off the hook since you disappeared off Minneapolis's radar scope and I called Sammy to tell him. You know you got a Christmas miracle tonight, don't you? We were all praying for you."

"Yes, Cheryl, I know I got a miracle, but the real miracle is even deeper. I'll tell you, if you care, when I get back. For now, have a great Christmas!! Good night!" I said with cheer.

The next number I dialed was my wife.

"Hello?" said Lisa. I was shaking.

With a cracking voice, I answered back, "Lisa it's me. I made it into a closed Air Force base. I'm safe." Immediately I heard her crying and also heard Anastasia, our daughter, saying "Mommy, mommy!!"

"Lisa, Lisa, please it's ok. I'm ok."

"Luke, you have no idea how hard I was praying after Sammy called and told me you had an emergency and that they lost radar contact. I thought I lost you. I was so scared, so scared. Lord, I am so thankful you are safe. What happened and where are you?" Lisa asked with her beautiful voice and soft tone.

"I'm at Wurstsmith Air Force Base, east side of Michigan. It's been closed for about a year according to an old timer here whose been helping me since I landed. I had a complete electrical failure and only had my battery for power. I had thirty minutes to land once my generator failed. I swear Lisa, I thought I was going to die. The weather here is horrible, but yet beautiful. It's snowing so hard and since it's Christmas it's so lovely, but I tried to get down below the clouds and find an airport but I couldn't. I was getting ready to eject when a F-4 came along side me and led me to the runway here. I swear, I don't how he found it. It was a miracle! When I find the guy who flew that jet, I'm going to buy him all the drinks he wants for a year. He saved me, he saved us."

"What do you mean saved us Luke? That was a funny thing to say." said Lisa, with curiosity. She's always had a remarkably high emotional IQ.

"Lisa," my voice was still cracking, and I, now, was on the verge of crying. "Lisa, I've not been a very good husband to you, and maybe not even the best father. I had some time to think about all of my faults tonight, the sin's I've committed in our marriage… the frequent drinking with the boys, carousing, roof stomping at 3 AM with the guys, getting crazy almost every Friday night the trips to other bases and getting wild there. God, I'm so sorry, I want to be a better husband, a better father."

I'm tearing up now, with alligator drops falling from my cheeks. "I want to be a better man, set a good example for our daughter, maybe even my bosses at work. I want to see Anastasia grow up. God, I've been such an asshole to you at times. I don't know why you stayed with me, but I thank God you did. Please forgive me…" I said dropping the mouthpiece from my face to wipe the tears away.

Lisa was now sobbing uncontrollably. I could hear her sobs and I could hear Anastasia saying "Mommy, mommy, don't cry mommy!"

I then heard Lisa saying tearfully to Anastasia, "I'm ok sweetie, mommy is just very, very happy. Mommy got her Christmas miracle tonight. Do you remember when we were in the backyard looking at the stars and mommy was praying to God for a miracle with your daddy?" Lisa did not wait for Anastasia to answer. "Well do you remember when we saw that big, bright shooting star fly across the sky? That was an angel rushing from heaven to answer my prayers. Mommy got her miracle tonight sweetheart, we both got a miracle. I'm so happy."

"Lisa, I need to ask you," I said, now composing myself, "When did you see a shooting star?"

"Oh honey, you make me laugh, with all this emotion and the revelations you're revealing to me, and you want to know when I saw a shooting star. Fighter pilots can be so unemotional and pragmatic."

I had to laugh, here I was crying on the phone with my wife, and maybe it's the first time I've shown true emotion with her and she calls me unemotional. I deserved that, because for far too many years I never let her, God, or anyone into my heart and head.

"No sweetheart, I'm curious, because I saw a shooting star about an hour and a half ago and when I followed it that's when I saw the Phantom, well F-4, appear on my right side. He led me to my landing. It was a miracle. I really hope I can meet that guy and thank him."

"Luke…oh my God….it was about an hour and half ago when I saw that shooting star and knew that you would be safe. I just never thought you'd actually love me again. I just wanted my fighter pilot back, I never thought I'd get the man I fell in love with and with whom I committed my life. I can't tell you how much I thank God for giving me the greatest gift I've ever been given…I got the husband I always wanted, the man I knew you were on the night of our first date. I thought I had lost you. I was going to leave you after the New Year. I couldn't take the coldness and indifference anymore. I knew you, the good you, that I fell in love with while I was in college was in there somewhere, I just didn't know how to reach you. I guess it took you staring at the abyss to realize how blessed you've always been. I love you…you need to get home soon so we can practice for another child."

"Honey, you have no idea how much I can't wait to prove to you how serious I am in changing. God pierced my heart tonight. He convinced me I needed to change. He opened a heart that was shriveling to death in the coldness of pride, loneliness, and a fear to let anyone see the real me, the insecure me. He has given me a second chance at a life I never knew I wanted, in the end, what I have really longed for but was afraid to admit. I can't wait to see you two again and to practice for the Anastasia's brother or sister."

"That must have been one hell of a flight!" Lisa said, now laughing.

"Baby, you have no idea. We'll talk more in depth when I can look at that beautiful face of yours. Merry Christmas Sweetheart…I love you. I'll call later before I go to bed."

"OH! Lisa! One more thing, do you remember that shrink we went to for marriage counseling a couple of years ago?" I asked.

"Yes, Dr Shaw, why?"

"Could you get in contact with him and tell him I'd like to begin seeing him. Just me though, OK?"

"Ohhhhhh Kaaayyyyy….Uhmm the last time we were there you got up and walked out of the session. Are you sure you want to see him. You know he's gonna' go places in your head where you don't want anyone to go," said Lisa, no doubt extremely skeptical of my sincerity.

"Lisa, if there was one epiphany I had on this flight, it is the need for me to dig deep into my very dysfunctional past with the help of an expert who's used to doing that sort of crap. Ya know, when you're standing on the edge of living or dying, you see the world, your life, through a very different set of lenses, and I didn't like what I saw. I've got some baggage from my past that I need to unpack and then throw away. Jesus girl, how the hell have you put up with me all these years? By the way, don't tell anybody about the shrink. I will tell the CO when I get back, but that's it."

"Man, I need a drink after this phone call. Don't worry, I won't spoil your macho fighter pilot image. It's nobody's business but our own." Lisa said laughing, adding, "I'll call him on Monday. I hope he doesn't drop dead when he hears why you want to see him, you didn't exactly impress him when you abruptly walked out a couple of years ago."

"Yeah, not one of my finer moments in life, I'm sorry about that," I said with deep regret.

"Luke, one last thing. You have no idea how much I prayed you would one day see the light God put in your heart. You are an incredibly kind and good person. Your parents' treatment of you doesn't have to define who you are or will become. In spite of your father's abuse, and your mother's neglect, you're not them. You are God's. He just used your parents to bring you into this world, not to be their clones. You came through your mother, not from her, and you are not obligated to be like either one of them. Do not kid yourself my darling fighter pilot, your road to growth will be painful at times; one night with a wonderful epiphany is just the beginning on a road less traveled, a road I am more than willing to walk side by side with you on."

"I've never been more serious about anything in my life Lisa, except the day I said I do to you."

"Ok, let's stop here, I don't know if I can take too much of the new you all at once," said Lisa laughing because of my last comment. "Let me gleefully ween myself off of the old you in the next couple days."

"I've got a very excited daughter who wants to bake daddy what she calls fighter pilot Christmas cookies, whatever they are, and after that I want to sit by the fire with a glass of wine and thank God again for the miracle He gave us tonight. I love you."

"I love you too babe, we'll talk in a bit."

After my very emotional phone call, I located my new found friend in the operations area sitting on a couch watching the weather channel. He stood up and greeted me with a smile as I walked towards him and I have no doubt he heard some of my phone conversation.

"The accommodations aren't that great but, we have a couple of rooms in the back with beds and ensuite bathrooms with showers. It's not the Ritz, but, it's better than sleeping on the couch. I'll be taking one of the rooms since I'm pretty much stuck here for the night myself. I called the misses to tell her. She's coming out with some food and will probably be staying the night too. She said she'll bring us some breakfast too."

"Jeezzz, how can she get here with all the snow?"

"Country girl, bit of a cowgirl. She drives a big F-350 dually, four-wheel drive. She was insistent. Stubborn girl, but she's had to put up with me all these years so I kind of let her do what she wants, it makes life easier."

"Okay, well I have to admit I'm starving. Any chance she's bringing adult beverages too?" I asked, secretly pleading.

Smiling, my friend said, "What's Christmas without adult eggnog?"

"Great," I said with a smile. I hate eggnog.

As the gentlemen continued talking, I noticed a wall in the operations room behind him that had many, many pictures of aircraft, pilots and other unknown, to me, people. I noticed, about eye level, a big plague kind of thing, in fact it was a very large picture frame with multiple pictures with-in its borders. I began to walk up to that set of pictures as his talking continued…talking which I couldn't really comprehend because I was so engrossed in the pictures I was seeing which were coming more into focus as I stepped closer to the wall.

"Who are these men in this photograph with the F-4?" I asked, pointing.

As he spoke, I moved even closer to the wall, eyeing with suspicion the photos. One picture showed an F-4 with a tiger painted on its nose. There was a man standing in front of the nose of the F-4, in his flight suit. It looked like a relatively old photograph.

"Who is this guy?" I asked again, trying to contain myself.

"Oh, there used to be F-4s that sat alert here, back in the early seventies. One night that guy, Captain Ryan, along with his backseater and another F-4 got launched while on alert to intercept an aircraft that was orbiting northeast of the field.

I remember that night well since I was on duty then and in this very building. It was a horrible night, kind of like tonight, actually, even stronger winds, come to think of it, it was Christmas Eve too. Huh, didn't think of that until now. Anyway, that guy there, Captain Ryan and his backseater, and the other F-4, joined up on the orbiting aircraft. Turns out it was a F-101 Voodoo from Niagara Falls that was heading into here to refuel when they had their radio and navigation gear fail. The Voodoo pilots knew if they orbited they would be intercepted, well they hoped anyway, and they were, thanks to Captain Ryan. He joined up with the Voodoo and led them back, with the Voodoo on his wing, and flew a PAR (Precision Approach Radar). How Captain Ryan got them in here, no one knew the weather was so bad. Blowing snow, it was a virtual whiteout when they landed, the Voodoo that is. Captain Ryan went around, after dropping the F-101 off, and told tower he was going to come back around for another approach. That was the last they heard from him.

The next day, after the storm began to clear, they started a search. They found the backseater floating in his raft in Lake Huron, freezing his ass off, but alive. He said they had a massive bleed air duct failure on missed approach after dropping the Voodoo off and it caused a lot of spurious electrical problems and their cockpit got uncontrollably hot. The backseater ejected once his boots began to melt from the heat. After three days of searching, they never found Captain Ryan or the F-4. The other F-4 diverted to another airport with better weather.

It was tragic. Everyone liked and respected Captain Ryan. I met him a couple of times. The other pilots said he was one hell of a good pilot, a natural. I remember seeing his wife and young child, a daughter, at the memorial for him, I swear the entire base went, he was so well liked. They said he was a very devout Christian, both a wonderful family man and a hard worker. Just doesn't make sense why good people die young, ya know?"

"Did all the aircraft that flew out of here have a tiger on the nose?"

"No. Well not when that picture was taken. They had just begun to paint tigers on the noses of the aircraft when the accident happened. That aircraft was the first one they painted, and it had his name on it. He was flying it on the night he disappeared.

"Jezzzz son, by the way you are looking at the photograph, I'd swear you thought you were looking at a ghost," said the old man cautiously.

"Ya' know if it was any other night of the year, I'd say I did think I saw a ghost, but, since it's Christmas Eve, I'm going to believe I saw an angel."

Made in the USA
Las Vegas, NV
21 November 2022

59929935R00049